THE MIND SURFER

Scenes from a journalist with psychosis

THE MIND SURFER

Scenes from a journalist with psychosis

Erica Crompton

Victorina Press

www.victorinapress.com

Typesetting and layout: Jorge Vasquez
Cover design: Clarrie-Anne Cooper

British Library Cataloguing in Publication Data
A catalogue record for this book is available from the
British Library.

ISBN: 978-19169057-8-8

Typeset in 11pt Garamond
Printed and bound in Great Britain by 4edge Ltd

Dedicated to my family and all the warriors who walk with this invisible illness

Prologue

> "Two pills for the evening,
> One for the day,
> between sane and insanity,
> to stay well each day."

The onset was fast. But not without a build-up of stress first (one of the main causes of relapse in psychosis) [1].

Although I felt I'd left the fear and dread in the past when I was first unwell aged 19, I'd been reading some anti-psychiatry textbooks over the last few months of 2008. Now we were in April 2009, and I had not been taking my medication.

It had been a stressful year. There was a move from London to my birthplace of Stafford to help care for my mum, endearingly known as 'Moomin Mama'. I had quit a good job at a Blue Chip retailer's head office, where I wrote about fashion. And I'd managed to secure a role at the local radio station in Staffordshire, where I wrote jingles and butt-clenchingly bad adverts.

Despite seemingly landing on my feet with work, over the following months I struggled with the breakdown of a romantic relationship, debt, a long-commute and, on top of it all, I had stopped my medication.

To help pay off my debts, which were in excess of £5K, I decided to take up a job offer in Southampton as a lecturer in journalism. Things really went wrong from there: I was sacked within two months and ended up feeling suicidal. I still wasn't taking my medication.

After that job went wrong, I ended up in a flat-share in a part of Birmingham punctuated with curry houses, fireweed and buddleia. I arrived from a tiny bed-sit in Shepherd's Bush that I left due to a discovery of bed bugs which had caused an outbreak of bites on my back. I was moving around – up and down - and not settling, never managing to get out-of-work benefits sorted, let alone find a rewarding job to stick at.

But it was in this bed-sit in Birmingham that I really started to become psychotic.

I had found this flat-share advertised on Gumtree as B13 but I discovered on moving in, that it was located in the Muslim belt, not the 'Muesli belt' of artists, musicians and bohemians who you might find in B13. I'd hoped to attend the contemporary dance class there. I'd viewed it late at night and the landlady had picked me up at the station and driven us there in such a way that I hadn't realised where we were.

I didn't mind. I saw the magic in my fabulous (if not isolated) integration with one of Birmingham's Muslim districts. The vast array of spicy fast-food takeaways, all fried within an inch of their lives and the many family-run clothes stores selling bejewelled Burkas to locals. Take-away, clothes shop, take-away, clothes shop – all piling up on top of one another along the heavily congested and littered Stratford road which runs two miles north into Birmingham City Centre.

It took just two weeks in this flat-share for me to completely undo. Initially it was problems with unsolved debt and not being able to access benefits. This kept me up at night and soon sleep was out of grasp as well as cash. While I was in my room, awake into the small hours, I had started researching unsolved crimes on the internet. I felt certain I'd been set up for all of them and could see various vigilante groups on Facebook encouraging me to kill myself. There seemed no way out for people like me. I'd further researched the story of Myra Hindley and how she'd never be released from prison and how if she was, everyone would still hate her.

I can recall queuing for my antipsychotic medication — ampisulpride — which I hadn't taken for the last 9 months. The GPs' reception was busy with families, many mothers holding not one but several babies, and I just seemed to be brushed off at reception. The place was in absolute chaos. I took it as a sign of my wrong-doing and went back to the flat. I started researching psychopathy, online, thinking perhaps it applied to me. That's when I began to notice signs and various vigilante groups on Facebook demanding my exile to Moscow. I then began my search for flights, and accommodation. I also started to pack my things. "Well, if most of Britain wants you in Moscow... best be off!"

While I had a history of psychosis I had been off medication and in denial about my experiences. On the following morning, I took one last attempt to get my medication and went down to the local A&E. But it was impossible, the psychosis had already taken a hold of me. I turned up at reception and told the lady that "I think I'm a sociopath". "Take a seat and a ticket." I looked at the queue and wondered how they'd feel about Britain's Most Wanted being sat next to them? I didn't need to think about it too long before I was on my way back to that room in the flat-share.

I did not know I was suffering from paranoid schizophrenia even though I had had a history of psychosis and indeed had previously been taking medication for the best part of a decade.

The kindness of strangers

Back at the house-share, where I was in hiding for the following two weeks, I had discovered mice in the kitchen. I'd all but lost my appetite and, like I said, the takeaways always offered up a cheap and swift dish that I'd never experienced before should I fancy some food. So I just decided to avoid the kitchen.

There were three others I was sharing this crumbling old house with and we epitomised multi-cultural Britain: a British Chinese couple and a first generation Indian from New Delhi, Varun and me, white British. I conversed very little during my brief time here. I can only recall Varun's name as he had a positive impact on my experiences. He showed me his room once and I immediately recognised the Ganesh deity he had lovingly set up on his bedside table which had now become a shrine complete with mini-prayer mat. "You know everything!" he replied to my deity ID. How wrong he was.

But it was Varun who helped a little during my time of need. He clearly had a very special sensitivity and knew I was in distress. Every morning he would go to his IT job in Birmingham City Centre, rising at 6.30am (our rooms were back-to-back and I would hear his alarm beeping) and leaving our flat-share around an hour later. Then, on his return at about 6.30pm, he'd watch a bit of TV in his room for an hour and then prepare his evening meal.

Before food preparation he'd gently knock on my door and quietly say my name:

"Ericaaah…" Then he'd kindly enquire if I'd like some food with him. "Ericaaaah, are you there? Can I make you some curry to share?"

As I felt I was such a big criminal I didn't want to bring shame to him so I'd decline. However, he'd always leave a vivid green, ceramic bowl of vegetarian curry and Basmati rice outside my room around 8pm. Knocking a little on my door to let me know it was there if I changed my mind.

You never forget kindness like this when you've been in a deep state of distress. He must have seen me briefly during the two weeks leading up to my suicide attempt, and seen how rapidly I was losing weight. I was a little under 10 stone when I entered the flat share and was a little under 8 stone once I departed in an ambulance. My flat-mate was there to feed me and just… to care.

Varun teaches us three things: firstly, that the kindness of strangers matters. And, secondly, that no matter how low you go and how barren, and burnt the ground around us seems, there is always love. And, thirdly, that once the suicidal crisis begins others are helpless to it.

I was at a talk about suicide and spirituality this month - a decade on from my crisis. Staff talked about how they always wonder if there was something they could have done differently when a patient is lost to suicide. They wonder if they could have just said this, or given that.

Varun did everything he could have done. He made a life-or-death situation more bearable. But really, when that state takes over, others are powerless to stop it unless the person in distress changes their mind about their attempted suicide themselves, as I did.

***

As I rushed over the littered pavement, I turned the key in the front door and rushed upstairs to make an attempt on my life. It was a ray of light through the curtains. I'd drank a poisonous concoction just minutes before I glimpsed the spring sun, powerfully penetrating the kitsch pink daisy printed curtains in my large bedroom in a flat share in a rundown part of Birmingham. That light spoke to me when no words could describe the state I'd been in over the last two weeks — funny then that it was also the wordless sun that communicated so much hope to me on that day. In a flash, I'd called an ambulance. I saw in that sunlight my youth. I was 29 years old and I'd seen my situation in an altogether different light after the rain and clouds of the last few weeks had lifted at some incredibly fortuitous timing. When I tell people about that moment they think the psychosis may have lifted but it hadn't. For the following weeks I believed any written words I read were written in an abstract way to hurt me —

including articles about Lady Gaga in The Daily Mirror, a newspaper I had previously contributed too. But the sunlight, at the moment in time when I needed it the most, warmed my cheeks and melted away some of the psychosis and all the self-loathing that brings for just long enough time for me to call 999. In psychiatry they call the ups and downs of 'paranoid schizophrenia', what I was later diagnosed with, as 'the course of the illness'. I call it 'the snakes and ladders of life'. Sure, I am up and down perhaps more than the most. However, at the end of the day when the sun is setting, I'm so glad for something as simple as a ray of spring sunlight during a crisis I had one day ten years ago. It saved my life and in hindsight I'm so glad it did for there's love, friendship and always others to help. After the dawn of a failed suicide, there is sunshine.

***

I would still love the chance to meet Varun and thank him for all he did for me. Maybe I'll start to look for him one day. But for now I'll leave it to Ganesh and the Gods to bless him accordingly, as they did me that day when an attempt on my life failed.

***

Over a decade on from these events I know very little about what happened to me. Psychosis can impact on my memory[2]. Some events from that time are only just becoming clear after much thought, a decade on.

Introduction

'To the winter and snow,
where my cats do go.
From the fear and dread,
where I once tread,"

The first sign of insanity was spending a week in bed, eating only Farley's rusks. It was a bid to 'rebirth' myself. A friend had told me in the student's union bar that I: "Would see the light." I reasoned with myself that to do this I would need to change what I ate, to change my consciousness. I also felt that if I ate baby food it would help me go back to the transcendental state of being near the womb. I didn't tell anyone what I was doing as I felt it was some sort of 'top secret' mission. And of course, it didn't work.

The year was 1999 and I was 19.

At around this time I was a second year University student studying fashion design in London. I was also on my work placement with a newspaper. A few months into my placement I was offered a job as an assistant on the fashion desk of an esteemed newspaper and I felt the regular routine would help stabilise my eating. 'Seeing God' had altogether put a stop to my eating for the last 7 months in a bid to radically change my consciousness. My weight had plummeted to just 5 stone and I had lost my periods. I began to crave stability and the newspaper, with its glamorous staff, seemed to offer me a safe space to do that.

For a short time I assisted the most perfectly beautiful and well-dressed fashion writer with research for her articles and on fashion shoots. This book wouldn't have been written without her for it was this lady who first encouraged me to write. "You're a natural", she chirped one day after I'd filed 100 words of copy for her Friday column. Today she's a successful business owner, mother and influencer and I find it comforting that success is granted to the deserving, happy people who work hard and are kind to people.

However, after a short while, I was promoted to a more stressful role and things really started to go strange a year or so into that job once I was on a full-time contract. It was around the events of 9/11 that things took a turn. Maybe it was the stress of working somewhere like Canary Wharf and the imminent threat of danger there. But I started to get creeping suspicions that my friends at the time (people I'd met in trendy squat parties) and pop star Rachel Stevens were terrorists and that I, as somebody working in Canary Wharf, was their next target.

They sent messages to their victims through songs on the radio and subtly planted into storylines on TV and on front pages of magazines. I was aware of their presence every time I got a cold call (they were testing my tone of voice and general mood), or a flicker of lost connectivity on the internet (testing my patience and volatility). Every time a wrong number popped up on my phone, I'd go into a blind panic – they were watching!

These terrorists had been setting me up for racially motivated sex offences, as well as a few unsolved murders ever since I attended a squat party in Shoreditch. They'd been deeply offended by my drunken behaviour and had sought revenge in the most callous way. They believed that I needed some violent assaulting to redeem myself from hell. And where did violent assaulting take place? Prison. And what would cause the most violence, outrage and shame – a sex offence.

Around this time, aged 21, I had the coil fitted and thought it was a Government camera ready to unmask a plan my friends had for me to blow-up the newspaper offices where I worked.

And then the times where I'd gone out socially but knew evidence against me was being constructed by friends – so I'd brought a Dictaphone to record the conversations in full, for my defence. Of course, this wasn't just a 'secret mission' now - this was high security, M15 type stuff, so hadn't confided in anyone.

My first diagnosis, with this in mind, was 'Paranoid psychosis' which has now been scrapped and changed to 'Delusional disorder'[3]. What both have in common, however, is the symptoms of psychosis which can be defined, in my case, as bizarre and persecutory beliefs and a loss of being in touch with reality.

According to Mind,[4] 'Psychosis' occurs when a person perceives and interprets reality in a different way to others. I suffered from delusions, or false beliefs, and other people suffer from hallucinations when the person with psychosis might see or hear things that others don't. Everyone is affected differently. My delusions were persecutory and frightening, terrifying even. A friend with psychosis, however, believes she's a God with superpowers and she finds her experiences not unpleasant. Of course, some people see and hear things or have strange beliefs and never come into contact with mental health services. But for a percentage of us, the thoughts and feelings are disturbing enough for us to seek support from the health services as I finally did a year after the aforementioned events.

It is said, according to Professor Stephen Lawrie, a psychiatrist from Edinburgh, that 4 in 100 people will experience psychosis at some point[5] – some people have one episode only, others have short episodes throughout their lives, and others may get progressively worse which is sometimes when we get the diagnosis of schizophrenia – when it persists.

Psychosis isn't a diagnosis in itself, it is more the symptoms of one of a few illnesses, including psychotic depression, bipolar disorder, schizo-affective and schizophrenia. However, there's a growing movement in mental health where service users and professionals feel there's so many negative connotations attached to the word, they'd rather use 'psychosis' to describe an experience than 'schizophrenia'.

Personally I use both − I use schizophrenia for the purpose of accessing healthcare and benefits, and psychosis socially or when meeting new people or at a job interview when I hope to minimize fear in others.

I do find the fear surrounding the name of my condition ironic, given how scared and terrified I am myself when I've been unwell.

There were many nights I spent during my first psychotic episode where I only slept and worked. When things really became acute I just worked and stayed up chain-smoking all night. Amid the silence of the small hours all I could hear were police sirens from the distant M6 motorway.

***

I'm Erica Crompton, a journalist and service user with experience of psychosis and a historical diagnosis of paranoid schizophrenia and, in The Mind Surfer, I aim to divulge everything I've learnt about psychosis and recovering from a severe mental illness over 2 decades, to help you lead a happier, more rewarding life.

Over 11 bite-size chapters I offer tried and tested advice for people going through a rough time with their mental health and talk about contributing factors that can lead to psychosis as well as practical tools to keeping well and staying sane.

This book is part memoir, part journalism and is for all people who may be at risk of developing, currently experiencing, or having experienced psychosis as well as family and friends who wish to help a loved one.

I've always maintained that low-mood and poor concentration

are the bread and butter of my condition, which, at the time of writing, is schizoaffective disorder. I've also found very few self-help guides specifically for people with psychosis.

With this in mind, The Mind Surfer is written like a magazine in small accessible chunks, which read like extended feature articles crammed with helpful tips and views which you can dip in and out of, for readers of all levels.

Like me, you're not alone if you have psychosis. In fact, 4 in 100 are said to suffer from it[5]. The impact of the illness on wellbeing and lifestyle means that often people with psychosis-related condition schizophrenia lose an average life expectancy of 14.5 years.[6]

So, this book is more relevant today than ever. With lifestyle and wellbeing advice to improve outcomes of people with psychosis, I write about all the techniques I've used to stay well myself and uncovered as a journalist living with psychosis for over two decades.

The Mind Surfer also includes illness self-management and other more formal approaches available on the NHS and other healthcare systems will be summarised in the first-person, by myself.

With expert advice straight from a person who has experienced psychosis, I pass on the tools to help people with psychosis and other severe mental illnesses manage their condition and recover a fulfilling and happier life, as well as giving tips on pitfalls that led to a diagnosis in the first place, such as intense stress and illicit drug use.

In the prologue and introduction, I explore the onset of psychosis and drill into what the experience felt like. We'll look at contributing factors to a psychotic episode - such as environmental and financial - and see how they can sadly lead to a suicide attempt. A stay at a mental hospital follows on and I'll look at what works and doesn't work in a crisis.

The bulk of The Mind Surfer looks at practical things that have helped me to stay well and recover from this relapse once I was stabilized on medication and discharged from hospital. After a little time at my father's house, I decided to convalesce on a Hare Krishna-run eco farm in Scotland. It's part of a scheme called 'WWOOF'[7] - World Wide Opportunities for Organic Farming - and it means that members can go and stay (and eat!) anywhere in the world for free, in exchange for their toil on the land.

I also found Mindfulness very helpful in bringing a sense of balance and equilibrium about myself after the dreaded hospital stay. Later, I tried Compassion Focused Therapy on the NHS which seriously improved the quality of my life and sense of happiness and wellbeing. Because being diagnosed with schizophrenia and being happy isn't an oxymoron.

After exploring what I did after a hospital stay, I delve into the causations of psychosis and write a little about experiencing adversity and how unhelpful relationships can be harmful and set us back in our recovery (or in some cases even cause psychosis). But don't despair - every cloud has a silver lining - and so long as I'm here to tell you my story I consider that a triumph in the face of adversity!

The concluding chapters of the book will look at where I am now - in a beautiful little cottage, set opposite a bowling green in a quaint Staffordshire village. I'll introduce you all to the two men in my life – Tom-cats Caspar and Winter.

My recovery and sense of happiness wouldn't be half as much fun without friends alongside me to walk with. In chapter 9, I'll look at peer support - where you find and meet people who share a diagnosis – with you for support.

Finally, I'll summarise everything for you to take home and end on a little bit about spirituality and how my own beliefs in spirituality, as make-shift as my Gods are, has helped give my life meaning and purpose as well as solace in times of need. We all go through ups and downs and for those with direct experience of psychosis, the journey can indeed be perilous. But we must move onwards and upwards bravely to ultimately find our tribe and ourselves.

Erica Crompton

Going Gaga - Crisis management, what helps and what doesn't help

'I wandered lonely as a ghost,
trapped on high o'er the sky,
When all at once the walls fell down,
It felt as hard as snow to cry;

In a flash, I'd called an ambulance. I saw my youth in the day's spring sunlight. I was 29 years old and I'd seen my situation in an altogether different light after the rain and clouds of the last few weeks had lifted at some incredibly fortuitous timing. The ambulance arrived within 10 minutes as I sat there in the stark reality and immediate aftermath of a suicide attempt. I did not know at this stage if I'd make it through.

Once a team of medics had arrived on site, they showed great compassion. I can remember a lady, she was young with mousy hair, asking me what I had done and how I was feeling. She was reassuring, too, telling me that everything was going to work out fine. She didn't challenge my delusions, but importantly she didn't seem to pass judgement on my crimes. "We all do things we deeply regret," she spoke to me softly, "you've done absolutely the right thing to call us."

I sat in the ambulance, it was moving now — I was reassured but unsure where we were heading and nervous about a media circus at the other end, to capture me, the wanted criminal. It was a confusing surprise when I was helped out my seat, and out of the back of the vehicle, some 10 minutes later. There were no cameras, no reporters, just a busy hospital. Here I was in my now-bleached stained, scruffy blue V-neck which had been stolen from the fashion cupboard of a previous job; and some 28 inch-waist Gap jeans which were now hanging off my hip bones.

I can't remember the walk to A&E or where the hospital was. I drifted in and out of consciousness.

I can vaguely recall being on a mobile hospital bed and being taken for an X-Ray to check if I was pregnant. Usually waits to be seen are a good few hours but I cannot remember if I was rushed through or simply unconscious during these first moments in A&E.

I woke after the X-Ray in a small but brightly lit curtained-off room to a doctor who wanted to take my blood. I felt certain he was poisoning me as he said he was putting me on some drip.

I didn't speak. I was still scared of a media circus forming outside. I'd called the ambulance during sometime in the afternoon. I was aware now that it was the middle of the night. Don't ask me how I knew, but I did.

I drifted back to sleep and woke in a seated area. It was the next morning. I started to read the papers for an update on my situation and they confirmed that my life was over. I wondered if I should make a run for it. I had thought Moscow was the place I should be heading after reading The Daily Mirror's campaign to send me there. I thought I'd ask a nurse about what was going on.

The NHS staff were busy and a nurse told me to hang on as she glanced at my notes. "We'll get you a bed soon. Please don't leave," she said. I wasn't sure. I thought I'd take a look outside and see if I could find a smoke.

It was dusk on my second day here. There were no cameras outside and I felt relieved. I don't know today, nor then, were I was. Ambulances were coming in but it wasn't overwhelmed. I saw some girls smoking round a big plastic bin outside the hospital doors. I waited for them to leave then went to pick up their fag butts and smoke them.

I was confused.

A nurse came out after a few minutes and I was back in the seated area. I had no phone, no money, just the clothes on my back and, being such a big criminal, I didn't wish to contact family or friends as I felt I would bring shame on them.

It must have been the middle of the night and I must have fallen asleep when I was approached by a nurse and given a bed. "Try to get some rest," she said, handing me a glass of milk. I thought she was giving me milk as I was a sub-species such as an animal, like a psychopath. I drank it anyway and took in the noises around me.

A man came in, handcuffed with two uniformed police officers. I figured they were waiting for me and wondered if I'd have died by the time they got to me. I closed my eyes and thought to myself that I could be dying. I guess at that point I wanted to die again.

The police had gone by the time I woke. Three doctors came in through the curtains and asked me how I was and to come with them.

We went into a little room, full of seats. They had folders and took notes as I told them what had been happening in the past few weeks. They nodded, not revealing too much and then took me back to my bed. I wondered if they were actually police.

Some half an hour later I was put in a wheelchair, my legs covered, as I found myself in the back of an ambulance again. It was late now. I may have been alone in A&E for 3 days. I didn't know where I was or where I was going. We arrived at a building and I was taken in. It was more relaxed than A&E. There was a big staff room overlooking a communal area, and doors that led to a garden. It smelled like urine.

First I went to the staff room and I was asked who my next of kin was. I told them my father was, but that I'd rather he not be contacted given the grossly criminal circumstances

(I didn't wish to bring shame on my family).

Then, I was taken to the communal area where a few patients were. A lady approached me and asked what I was doing there. "I'm Britain's most wanted criminal," I told her. She squealed with laughter and offered me a cigarette. I went outside to smoke it.

I was then shown my room, a clean and spacious single room with the Wordsworth poem, Lonely as a Cloud, printed out and left on the table by the single white bed. I felt it was a sign I was going to be very lonely.

A nurse came in with some tablets, I took them. If I was going to get out it would be for good behaviour. Or was my sentence one of madness without actually losing my mind? I wasn't sure but I took the tablets and had a good night's sleep. I still felt scared.

Dawn broke. There are always a few moments on waking where everything is ok and I'm not struggling so much. A few seconds later, the conspiracies return.

They had newspapers on the psychiatric ward and I had gathered them together to piece together the stories about my crimes and subsequent capture. There was a picture of Lady Gaga in the Daily Mirror newspaper that morning. She had a "little monsters" tattoo that the paper was writing about. On seeing this I immediately thought that it is written for me, and me alone. That I was the 'little monster' and that it was written to tease me about the crimes I believed I'd committed.

"You've got a visitor," I heard a nurse say from over my shoulder as I read the headlines.

It was my Dad with my credit card and some clothes. Years later he said I appeared to be a "lost soul" back then. I don't remember what we spoke about or how long he stayed.

I was here for just two nights. Because I'd lived in Southampton prior to the Birmingham flat-share, my medical notes and care team were based there. I'd been put back on my anti-psychotic medication here but now I had to go to Southampton where I would stay in a mental hospital for one week.

It was the run up to the general elections when I was hospitalised and, despite taking little interest in current affairs, I found myself at the centre of the politician's campaigning.

I couldn't watch the TV or news during my stay as I felt certain the BNP politician Nick Griffin was a metaphor for myself and my crimes.

My Dad tells me that he and his girlfriend came to visit me during this week. I have no recollection of this. I do remember feeling uncomfortable here and eventually was allowed out, still unwell.

My Dad collected me. He played 'Can you read my mind' in the car home and I felt he was giving me a message that mind reading is real, but I felt comforted to be in his Alfa Romeo with heated seats on this cool, fresh spring morning.

I had made it through the crisis, and while I felt at the time my life was over, really it was just about to begin.

Erica Crompton

The Hare Krishna farm - to Glasgow...

When toiling the land can be grounding,
And the chants of the monks resounding,
When all you need is a lift to your feet,
The Krishna Devotees are ready to greet.

"Flight 0892 to the boarding lounge. That's 0892 now ready to board."

I'd heard the announcement loud and clear for a local flight to Glasgow from Birmingham International Airport, an ugly concrete mass of 1970s Brutalism punctuated with aimless crowds, none of whom seemed to know where they were going. Twenty minutes before the gate closes.

"Plenty of time", I thought as the artificial lighting on the ceiling moderated the noises below.

I made my way to the designated smoking area, where I'd been chuffing away regularly for the last 2 hours.

"Plenty of time."

I sat under a bus shelter, now for smokers, smoking my cigarette and wondering if I too should make my mark by burning a stub in the plastic of the shelter. Then, I tried to stop thinking altogether to shut out the noises around me. Crowds make me panic. So do flights. And besides:

"Plenty of time", I decided to pull out second cigarette before I meandered back to the boarding room to board my short flight. My cigarette tasted good, a little like the first of the day. My mind fell quiet as I focused on the billowing smoke plumes to take my mind off all the people. Then, without making a burn-mark, I finally felt relaxed enough to return to the gate to board. I pulled my boarding pass out my bag as I made my way back inside the airport and to the electronic ticket scanner.

Damn things broken. So (slightly panicking now) I go to the nearest help desk. "Sorry, gates for flight 0892 closed about 2 minutes ago."

"In the midst of winter, I found there was, within me, an invincible summer." – Albert Camus.

For me the best periods of time are always off-set by a troubling start. Once I was finally enveloped beneath the moody Scottish skies (there was another flight 4 hours later), I found my own summer in Lesmahagow, a small village 45 miles south of Glasgow Airport.

I had finally managed to find the monk, Stevie, who was picking me up at the airport in a clapped-out blue and green Nissan Micra.

Modern life isn't lost on the monks. Many have Smart phones and motors prove an important part of running the eco farm. George, the head monk at the farm drives a 7-seater dark blue 2004 Land Rover as he says it does the job of three smaller vehicles on the farm. Before he became a monk, George trained as a mechanic. Today he uses those skills to fix old cars "with spanners… it's better for the environment to keep old cars working," he says.

As an expert in meditation, George says of mindful driving: "If we keep in mind we're all imperfect then when someone cuts us off we can stay calm and understand we don't know what's going on in that person's life. I avoid road rage knowing that getting angry won't help others or myself. I wave and smile at people in my car. If I'm stuck in traffic I'll try chanting to help me keep calm… anxiety doesn't move traffic."

I was booked to stay here for 3 weeks and as the Micra spluttered up to the farm's entrance I wondered what I'd let myself in for.

This was a spiritual eco-farm run by Hare Krishna monks which I'd discovered through Worldwide Opportunities for Organic farming (WWOOF).[7a] Also known as the 'Krishna Eco Farm' or Karuna Bhavan, the land's home to a pre-fab temple and community of over 30 people, made up Hare Krishna monks, families, and volunteers like me.

The farm sits atop a steep hill and the walled gardens either side of the winding path are flanked intricate stone monuments that wouldn't look out of place in India. On entering, you'll find a navy and white 'Karuna Bhavan' sign letting you know you're in the right place and acting as a gate to the women's 'ashram' (ashram meaning home in Indian). The men's ashram sits slightly behind the women's just to the left. There's a no-sex rule on the site.

Accommodation is basic, and shared. I found myself with a three-bed room all to myself. It's warm inside, and spacious. Large posters of the little blue Krishna God in jewelled colours decorate the wooden walls along with stenographs of elephants and peacocks. The bedding is all floral fabrics in a rainbow of pastel and primary colours. I feel I could be in a real Indian ashram with all this 1970s wicker and wooden floors, though a glance outside at the plump and heavy Scottish rain clouds reminds me I'm not.

The WWOOF scheme means you must help harvest crops for 6 hours a day, 5 days a week in exchange for a bed, and 3 meals (much of which are made from the crops here). It's a Mecca for homeless people and also those just out of prison who are building their lives from the bottom, up.

You earn your keep here and learn as you earn. I saw it as a 'Ground Zero' operation having just been discharged from hospital with no savings or income. It was here I set up my state benefits for support with people off work with an illness. I found it a great place to nurture my mental health and get back on my feet. Bhakti the Head Gardener here: "We do some horticultural therapy here. People with mental health problems come along and we encourage them to grow food. It makes them feel more positive."

For those who don't want to do the farming you can pay a token as small as £10 a night for the same deal and explore Glasgow and surrounding areas if you're prepared to put in a few hours travel in (the eco farm is a 45 minute bus ride from Glasgow City Centre). People who stay should always be mindful of the house rules though such as no alcohol, no meat, and (as previously mentioned) no sex.

The Hare Krishna monks are dotted around the grounds in their orange robes from 3am when their meditations at the small, refurbished temple. You can often hear them chanting "Hare, Hare!" They mostly cut lithe, warm figures with their shaven heads fully focused on their work. The farming is performed with devotion for the Hindu God Krishna and forms a crucial part of the devotees' lifestyle. They refer to it as 'Bhakti yoga' where the aforementioned Head Gardener gets his name.

You'll often find Bhakti working in one of two large green houses that sit aside the women's ashram, a little further up the hill and framed by a winding path to the temple right at the top. Chanting, meditation and yoga take place in this colourful and diminutive temple with intricate carved deities covered in garlands which are made on-site with the marigolds that Bhakti and the volunteers' harvest.

It's so colourful and yet peaceful at the farm. I've since returned one summer for their Hindi Festival of Lights, known as "Holi". With monks and friends, we threw coloured paint at each other while singing and dancing. The best part was sitting in the farm grounds around a campfire with sheep until late.

Breakfast, lunch and dinner follow the early birds at 8.30am, 1.30pm and 7.30pm. The food is all vegetarian and much produced on site such the spinach and the potatoes. They call it 'Prasadam' and it tastes a little like curry – think Saag Paneer rather than vindaloo as it's all very mild.

Healthy eating is welcome on my stay here after the limp and lifeless food offerings at the mental hospital in Southampton. After 5 days without coffee, booze and meat I do feel energised and healthier. The eco farm was just what I needed after hospital and to nurture myself and feel more grounded. I even wrote a review to mark my 30th birthday here. It was a 5-page splash in Spirit & Destiny magazine: "Will Erica find enlightenment for this milestone birthday… or just mud?" read the strap line alongside a flattering photo of me pulling up some spuds. My editor at the magazine said I was "a good sport," for writing such an honest account of my time and situation. The monks later said this would be good for my "Karma" and I also received a very "Karmic" £300 for the article from the glossy-yet-spiritual magazine. Good vibes can live on through the wildest of winters and even in a summer that follows on from a spring stay in hospital.

Erica Crompton

Finding Mindfulness

"Mindfulness is the awareness that comes from learning to pay attention in a particular way in the present moment and non-judgmentally to things as they are,"
(Jon Kabat-Zinn)

The farm and its inherent 'zen' brings me to my experience of meditation. It's been almost 6 months since I was diagnosed with paranoid schizophrenia. And I've battled with various diagnoses since. More recently I've stabilised on medication and am now 'officially' schizo-affective. I'm told that's because there's an added mood element typified by periods of over excitement, mild depression and a sporadic sleeping pattern.

I've tried many alternative therapies to help with these, along with taking my medication, to help – such as Traditional Chinese Medicine and yoga as well as the 'Bhakti yoga' I learnt on the Krishna Eco Farm – which have all worked in some way. Mindfulness is the practice of intentionally bringing attention to something in the here and now, whilst letting go of judgements.

Mark Williams is Professor of Clinical Psychology at the University of Oxford's Department of Psychiatry and co-developer of Mindfulness-based Cognitive Therapy (MBCT). Explaining Mindfulness in terms of neurology, he says: 'There are two sorts of issues that research on Mindfulness focuses on. We now know that eight weeks of MBCT cuts the risk of future depression by 40-50 per cent in those who have recurrent depression. The second issue for research is how it works – researchers examine the mechanisms underlying Mindfulness to ensure that there are genuine changes happening, not just placebo. Most interesting are the changes in the brain when people meditate – actually shown on brain scans. For example, studies from the States show that the amygdala, the flight/fight reaction part of the brain, is over active in people who rush about and worry a lot. When we are stressed, the amygdala switches on too easily and stays on too long, causing yet more stress and exhaustion. Research shows that Mindfulness helps reduce activity in the amygdala, allowing us to distinguish real from imagined threats.

'The other area in the brain that Mindfulness works on is the insula - known to switch on when we feel emotions in the body. The insula is also critically involved in helping us feel empathy for others. We now know that people meditating show important changes in the insula. Usually activity in the insula is closely coupled with activity in other parts of the brain involved in thinking. When we experience an emotion we not only feel body sensations but also start thinking - telling a story about ourselves or others - and we can see this connection in the brain. Problems arise when thinking turns to over thinking - when the stories we tell become hijacked by anxiety and depression so they become negative. After Mindfulness training, we see activity in the insula becoming uncoupled from the part of brain that underlies this over-thinking, so the one doesn't automatically lead to the other: we can feel things, without starting to brood about them. Mindfulness doesn't suppress the thoughts or feelings but puts a gap between one and the other so we have more choice. It's like a pause button that slows the process down.'

Mindfulness is the practice of intentionally bringing attention to something in the here and now, whilst letting go of judgements. It has been used increasingly to assist those experiencing mental health problems as it is an approach which helps individuals tolerate being in the presence of their thoughts and feelings, rather than fighting or fleeing from them.

Dr Rachel Lucas, Consultant Clinical Psychologist for South Staffordshire and Shropshire Healthcare NHS Foundation Trust, runs a Mindfulness programme and said: "In our service we have begun to offer mindfulness in both community and inpatient settings in groups and individually. Although this is a newly developing approach for our service, those experiencing it have described it as being very beneficial."

While the practise is currently enjoying a renaissance, it's been around for some time. I first try dialectical behaviour therapy (DBT) - one of many Mindfulness variants – as an inpatient at Royal South Hants Department of Psychiatry in April 2010, now called Antelope House.

Dr Vivia Cowdrill, consultant psychologist at Antelope House says: 'DBT is a treatment for people who are often suicidal. It's based on a brand of CBT (cognitive behavioural therapy). Neurologically, it's through behaviour you create new neuro-pathways in your brain which enable you to behave differently. Acceptance as part of DBT comes from Mindfulness where the individual is not only creating a new skill but a new attitude towards life. And this is what is drawn from Buddhism.'

While I was there, a staff nurse would facilitate a group of around 12 inpatients all attending on a voluntary basis, around twice a week. At the time I thought I was deeply psychotic and suffering from the belief I was a criminal. While DBT Mindfulness doesn't resolve my false beliefs what it does do is minimise the feelings of terror that come with believing everyone's out to get you.

Janet Jones, a patient at Antelope House, was diagnosed with severe clinical depression. After being sectioned four times in early 2008, she was introduced to DBT. She tells me: 'I was very sceptical about Mindfulness at first, I thought it was some new age hippy thing. But soon my approach changed and I found my life improved. Mindfulness is the skill that has had the most impact on my recovery. It has given me more control over my life.'

It's grown in importance in modern psychology in this decade and is found in various fields such as in psychotherapy, coaching, workplace stress management and performance enhancement.

"It is a great skill that teaches us to untangle from challenging or undesirable thoughts or emotions and make more effective choices in our lives. Research shows that practicing mindfulness regularly can help people manage chronic pain and symptoms of stress. It has also been shown that mindfulness-based cognitive therapy can reduce the likelihood of experiencing a depressive relapse," says Dr Christodoulou from South London and Maudsley NHS Foundation Trust, adding: "Mindfulness can also be beneficial to individuals in the general population by improving immune system functioning, enhancing psychological wellbeing, increasing resilience, and improving concentration and general effectiveness."

With all this science backing up the practise I sought help from private psychotherapist Sally Stubbs (NHS waiting lists for Mindfulness can currently be very long). Her unique practise is coined 'Rapha therapy'. Like Mindfulness it takes some of its many cues from ancient Eastern traditions such a Buddhism but more importantly claims to address the root causes of false beliefs – talking directly to the subconscious that drives our thoughts. Her practise, like CBT, is not pure Mindfulness, but a kind of guided meditation and exploration of the subconscious.

Yet from the outset I feel like Sally is gold. Consider this: the success of a Government campaign like Time to Change has successfully reduced stigma which means many more people are coming forward with mental health problems. In addition, NHS cuts severely affecting these 'Cinderella services' means waiting lists for treatment are now much longer.

A profound moment in my three-day therapy with Sally comes in recognising a root cause in my false beliefs. Through her technique we pinpoint the disturbance in my thoughts as a loud internal dialogue I often feel present. Once I tell Sally about this voice, she locates it in my past and uses a 'magic bow and arrow technique' to resolve the past issue and thus the historical moment of trauma which has caused me to think in a certain way. We do a lot of this type of work together and I do leave after my three day stay feeling more confident and wholly relaxed. I'm not the only person who has found this method useful.

Diagnosed in her teens with an eating disorder, Diana had twice been hospitalised with morbidly low weight. She had anorexia, and later bulimia. Aged 28, Diana worked with Sally and they discovered that, aged 13, she had been utterly shocked to find her parents were about to split up. Her eating disorder was an unsuccessful attempt to gain control over her world which has been shattered. Sally brought resolution to her needs for control, telling me: 'We found an understanding that what she needed was an inner sense of stability. We cannot control the world around us, but we can gain an inner sense of Mindfulness control."

As with various alternatives I've received, I feel my practises in DBT and with Sally all have their uses in minimising low-mood and anxiety long-term. But I am not about to ditch the medication just yet. As Dr Tamara Russell says: "These things can take years of practise. Sometimes several years. A 3-day programme is just a stepping stone."

I've since expanded my Mindfulness practise, and a cheaper version than going privately. Since meeting Sally I've discovered that YouTube has many free Mindfulness recordings and my favourite after trying a few are ones by Michael Sealey.

Sealey, like Sally, produced guided meditations of Mindfulness but combines them with his expertise as a hypnotherapist – this makes for a super-soothing voice. Of course, even after years of sporadic practise I'm not about to ditch my meds but I find a 35-minute guided meditation by Sealey is powerful enough to settle me when my mind is racing or help me get to sleep if I'm struggling. I also do these meditations for pleasure sometimes, too – the pleasant angelic lull of the background music is extremely soothing.

The effect a half-hour meditation has on me is like that of reading in bed for a couple of hours. I've tried the Head Space app too, which has been made by a former Buddhist monk. I signed up for a year's subscription and did 10 minutes a day for a year – sometimes more, sometimes less. The nice thing about the HeadSpace app is that it tracks progress and totals hours spend meditating. I did almost 2000 hours in total in the year I subscribed. It helped keep my responses to the ebbs and flows of the passing weeks measured.

The last type of Mindfulness I tried was with a group of 6 other patients as part of group Cognitive Behavioural Therapy. At the end of each 2 hour session we all took part in 10 minutes of NHS-produced Mindfulness designed with patients with psychosis in mind. This was great and we were all given the CDs we listened to, to take home and practise. A short burst of time like this is easy to incorporate into the day or evening. And it feels good that these meditations have the 'official' NHS approval for patients with psychosis.

Overall, my experience with Mindfulness has been helpful in 'letting go' or sitting with uncomfortable feelings that accompany my mental illness and accepting these feelings too shall pass. Ride on, and peace out.

My experience of Compassion Focused Therapy

With loving kindness,
did the Bodhisattvas sing,
with the greatest compassion;
we will all be kings.

Maybe it's the Buddha statues I grew up with in my middle-class home in the Staffordshire countryside. Maybe it's the books I read by the Dalai Lama when I first moved to London aged 18. Or maybe it's a core belief I inherited. But I feel deeply drawn to Eastern-inspired therapies, especially Buddhism.

I didn't take part in the Krishna meditations on the farm, I found it was best to get stable on medication first which took six months. After a year in recovery now I was finally able to access talking therapy on the NHS. My psychologist let me choose the type of therapy I had and as soon as she told me about CFT – Compassion Focussed Therapy, I knew that was what I wanted to try. With its roots in Buddhism and with my good experience on the Krishna Eco Farm, this felt like something I could really get enthusiastic about.

So, over the course of two years, I had weekly to twice-monthly CFT. When I started I was asked what I'd like to achieve with my sessions and I had hoped for a couple of outcomes – to improve my low-mood, to find out what caused my psychosis and to find ways to prevent it in the future.

By far the best part of the therapy was the outcome to improve my mood. My medication can leave me fairly lethargic and I sleep a lot. It's not unusual for me to sleep 9 hours a night and lie-in for further on waking. Prior to therapy I'd been getting really down about this, but my therapist taught me that "It's okay to stay in bed." This was a revelation and her permission to not just stay in bed but to be happy about it improved my mood no-end.

Although this therapy is still relatively new, I've met others who have benefited from it. Like many girls in their teens, Justine loved nothing better than a night out clubbing – until she was attacked one night by a bouncer after having her drink spiked. Now, she lives with anxiety as a result. But the CFT inspired in parts by the Dalai Lama is helping her overcome her fears too.

Twenty-two year old Justine, from Surrey, was just 14 when she was attacked in a club and today, while most of her friends are out partying, she suffers from excruciating anxiety.

Today Justine's fears are as real as ever. While she manages to hold down a job at a university and has recently adopted a tabby cat, her life has still been dogged by that incident all those years ago.

She says: "I have really worrying and intrusive thoughts about my cat during the day." Recently Justine started a course of CFT – compassion focused therapy - privately, with London-based therapist Matthew Brown of the HS Focus group.

"I've had six hourly sessions of CFT and it's not only helping me with my anxiety, it's also made me realise the reasons why I feel fear in some situations. We've concluded that I'm better at imagining I'm speaking to friend or someone else when dealing with my thoughts. If I think about putting a stranger in a situation, I imagine how they would deal with it. With CFT it's not just about discovering the reasons behind my actions (we spent the first two sessions focusing on my childhood), it's also about showing compassion to myself if I'm having an off moment."

CFT therapist Chris Irons says: "CFT was developed in the UK by Professor Paul Gilbert, a Clinical Psychologist in Derby. In many ways this has been an evolving process in Paul's work over 30 years but started to take shape as a 'therapy' in the last 15 years."

"It's mainly practiced in the UK, although, increasingly, we are training people across the world, including France, Germany, Italy, Portugal, Australia, New Zealand, the United States and many of the Scandinavian countries.

"In terms of evidence, this is developing. As a relatively young psychotherapy we are working hard to show that this approach has something important to offer people. As it stands at the moment, there has been one successful randomised control trial of CFT. The research evidence for CFT is currently small but growing, and our findings so far have been promising - in general they have found a reduction in symptomology in people with a particular 'diagnosed' mental health problem. The research findings have shown that difficulties that are common in many mental health problems often all reduce, on average, following a CFT intervention."

Of his therapy, Dr Paul Gilbert tells the Mail on Sunday: "People often get the wrong idea about compassion, they think it's just kindness or gentleness. In fact, the key quality of compassion is courage because compassion is a sensitivity to suffering in self and others with a commitment to try to prevent and alleviate it. So compassion is based upon caring motivation and that's not always easy because often we want to turn away from the things that hurt us or cause us pain. But turning into them without compassion is very tough."

Compassion therapist Matthew Brown, who treated Justine, says his practice has its roots in Cognitive Behavioural Therapy, known as CBT. He says:

"Compassion therapy's original grounding is in CBT but it draws on Buddhist ideas of compassion – like the Dalai Lama's definition. We recognise the suffering in ourselves and others. It requires you to be aware of your thoughts in the present moment and in that way it has links with Mindfulness. "I apply compassion to my own life. It's very human and taps into common humanity: though this practise isn't religious in the slightest it does draw on Buddhist psychological elements." Paul Gilbert developed the therapy for people with high levels of self-criticism, shame and who'd had traumatic experiences or unpleasant upbringings. Over five years, it's evolved to treat people with different issues, one being anxiety – the threat emotion – that Justine has.

"Together, we learnt that that threat emotion is actually very natural and we've normalised the experience of anxiety by locating it in past experiences. By doing so, we're able to sooth and manage, knowing that's there absolutely nothing wrong with experiencing this."

In the psychological model, in general, therapists will spend a lot of time understanding people's past experiences, not just childhood but things happen that have impact and then affect us later in life. It goes across diagnosis as this doesn't inform us to people's unique experiences.

Justine now knows that the anxiety she faces is not her fault and she can also understand why she experiences it, based on her past.

Personally speaking I found researching past reasons for my psychosis a little unhelpful. The psychological model in general, which CFT also employs, often looks at negative experiences in childhood and relates them back to present day problems. I found this unhelpful because it felt like I was engaging in a 'blame game' with people in my past. What we discussed in therapy was vague memories from childhood and while childhood adversity is established to have an impact on adult mental health, the connections I made between past and present – they're not necessarily facts and certainly didn't help nurture good relationships in the present.

What works best for me is to keep a positive outlook on life and relationships in general to enable me to create a brighter future. And to some extent CFT did help me to do this.

One of the best exercises I did as part of my therapy was to keep a 'Happy Book' – a compilation of any complimentary emails or kind texts. Birthday cards, notes or entries on social media that brought a smile to my face. I printed and kept them all for my 'Happy Book'. That was in 2015 and I still keep the book today. It never fails to bring a smile when I'm feeling low. I read it page to page and feel good. It's a great resource for anybody who would like a boost, too – not just those of us in therapy.

The song 'Happy' by Pharrell Williams was getting air-time on every radio show when I was undergoing treatment. It seemed apt and still does. And that's always the desired destination of therapy whether you have a mental illness or not. To feel happy.

Fashion... and other fairy tales

Fashion's parody
Fashion's comedy
But it will make you feel good
It will make you feel good.

Around my 18th year, like Justine, I was down 'sarf. And, like Justine, I struggled most with my mental health during those formative years. I'd had a really tough time with scary Devil Wears Prada fashion lecturers and editors.

For example: "Have you always been that thin, Erica?!" Jane bellowed through the length of the classroom, and over the aggressive metal sewing machines.

Jane was a lecturer and head of fashion at a redbrick university in London. The university was well-regarded and Jane knew it. She bellowed at all the students and looking back you'd think we were training to be surgeons, not sugar-plum fashion designers.

The site was like a conservatory, the large windows in the whitewashed room to the left were letting all the sun in.

Jane was so loud and assuming - I swear I could have seen the threads on the many sewing-machines here shiver in the light as she walked past.

A few third year students looked to her as she spoke to me, and then looked to me for my reaction. The machines in the next room, used by the second years, hummed over my silence. I shrugged, and feeling humiliated slinked off to my corner with a few other first years in one of three open white spaces where we studied.

I'd always shrugged off comments about my five stone frame.

I had stopped eating for several months during my first and later second year on this course as I thought it would change my consciousness so I 'would see the light,' Of course, looking back, it was a first episode of psychosis. But, at the time, I didn't know people's thoughts could become unwell.

As Jane hovered, I remained silent about it and buried myself in work. And here on my white plywood desk beneath a mood board of magazine cuttings which I compiled there was plenty of work. Everyone had one of these cabin-like work spaces to decorate with magazine cuttings or scraps of fabric brought from Soho.

Jane was having none of my silence though. She had found a bone to pick with me on this day and was holding onto it like a tenacious bulldog. She breezed her way to me, fabric swatches and mood boards lifting in the breeze as she walked past.

She was a big woman, but she wore draped and loose fit clothes to disguise it. Long cashmere ponchos and wide, very long cotton pants, all in loud contrasting patterns and clashing colours. It gave the effect of her hovering as she walked. And here she was hovering towards me, poncho swaying with each step and the clashing green and pink getting louder. "I say poor thing, what are you working on?" she continued, not quite as loud as before.

"I'm hand embroidering a dove. It's for my Grandad, he's not very well." I replied, as polite as I could.

"Aaaand?"

"He's in hospital" I explained hoping to satisfy her.

It was really no good though, she was shaking her head as the words shook out of my mouth.

"You know if you want to work in fashion you must get

better at communicating! If you were being interviewed by the press… Well, this explanation really wouldn't do!"

If it were possible to lose a foot in height, I may have at that moment. I was stooped so low at my desk in despair. Maybe she picked up that this wasn't the body language of a roaring successful fashion designer in the making. Or maybe I was doing my Grandad a great disservice with such a pithy description of the dove I was embroidering for him. "Think about it. You seriously need to improve dear!"

I lasted just 2 years at this university before dropping off to work full-time. I thought about going back, but shudder at the thought in hindsight.

The Daily Telegraph

And so, after completing and passing my 2nd year of a BA(Hons) in fashion design I headed into the world of work. As part of the course I did a work placement at The Daily Telegraph fashion desk, and after two fun weeks had bonded with staff there enough to warrant a job offer. I stayed on the fashion desk for just under 3 years.

Fashion reaches audiences academia and healthcare cannot. For example, according to The Mental Health Foundation, almost half of British girls aged 17 to 21 have suffered with mental illness[8]. If you're working in a creative job you're 25 per cent more likely to suffer from mental illness. And a 2012 study conducted by Model Alliance revealed that around 68.3 per cent of models suffer from depression or anxiety[9].

So, I'm not alone in feeling fashion may be a cause for good, empowering people to feel great about how they look while starting conversations. Wear Your Label, a style collection in Canada, is designed by Kayley who has battled an eating disorder, and Kyle living with Generalized Anxiety Disorder and ADHD. Another label close to my heart is Schizophreic. nyc[10] who's tee slogan "don't be paranoid, you look great!"

chimes with me. Other designers toting the mental health slogans include Fandabby.net[11] who use positive colour psychology in their genderless tees.

Another draw cord of fashion, for me, is that it can help you create a new identity outside of a diagnosis. It can give you the option to be a punk or a bohemian rather than John Psychosis!

So, here I am with a collection of signature bright colours for men and women, including two fruity bracelets, a man's t-shirt in royal blue, a women's t-shirt in neon pink, a printed canvas and a glittering clutch.

Fairy tale fashionistas

Still in London, in 2006, I'd just graduated in journalism and got a job in a business-to-business communications agency as a receptionist, and was hoping to work my way up as a writer. It was a low-paid job, but it was a start. The few weeks I spent there were pain-staking. It felt so far away from where I wanted to be.

One time I hadn't changed the toilet roll in the bathrooms fast enough. In fact I didn't even realise it was up to me to keep the toilets fresh. But the Head of Writing came out the toilet with wet hands and flicked all the residual water at me, sat in reception. Everyone laughed and I was mortified. Incidents like this happened increasingly as the weeks started to pass.

On my twelfth week I was fired for making too many mistakes. I cried and cried as I was told by the office manager, on a Friday, after everyone else had left. It was around the same time I was starting to open up to people about my diagnosis of Paranoid Psychosis and I needed support more than ever yet wasn't finding it easily. Thing is I had rent to pay and my partner at the time wasn't willing to help. He blamed me for making the mistakes.

So on the Saturday morning after being fired I printed off my CV and dropped it off to a handful of local pubs with a covering letter requesting bar work. As luck would have it, a pub got back to me. It was a little gnarly working there on weekday nights – a denizen of drug dealers and bitter, drunk doctors – but it would help pay the bills and I now had the day free to try and break into journalism again. I'd hoped to be writing stories now with my degree in journalism.

One of the editors I sent my CV to, was Molly, the lovely fashion writer I worked with at The Daily Telegraph. She'd since married and changed her name. Yet she remembered me and offered me a few days as her assistant on the shopping pages of a glossy newspaper's supplement. I leapt at the chance. I remember meeting her after a few years and she had this immaculate office covered in snazzy art work and strewn with all the latest clothes people had sent her to feature in her pages. My role was only sending clothes back to people but it felt so much nicer than pouring pints to drunks, and it paid better too.

One of the people I was returning a fetching mint-on-olive polka dot jumper with pussy-bow to was none other than Mandi – often described as London's most 'on it' fashion publicist. She didn't remember me from The Daily Telegraph but she was impressed with my phone manner and invited me to go and see her in her office the following morning.

The work with Molly was awesome and enjoyable but sadly not regular enough to quit the pub work. However Mandi was offering regular work as her office manager alongside all London's hottest designers. I went from being soaked in toilet water by a condescending nobody to calling up British Vogue's fashion writers with research and partying with Gareth Pugh in a wedding dress Mandi loaned me one evening.

I often think back to this short transitory period in my life. I was devastated when I got fired as a receptionist, but it turned out better paid, more glamourous work with some of my favourite, strong fashion women awaited me. (POSSIBLE REWRITE)

Don't let set-backs get you down as you never know what's around the corner. Your life can always change for the better.

Pretty things

Forays into the fashion worlds are further from my mind these days, but it's worth remembering and is a nice hobby now and then.

The fashion degree I studied when I was at university was quite 'arty' and I have also found Fine Art helpful in my journey. The biggest drawback of being diagnosed with schizophrenia is the suicide statistics. 1 in 100 people suffer with schizophrenia, 10.1% of all suicides had schizophrenia. Suicide rate in adults with schizophrenia was 6.8/1000 people/year.[12] While depressing, I can't help but be drawn to the most cited quote all the world over: "To be or not to be, that is the question." An acknowledgement echoed and elaborated on by Albert

Camus in the Myth of Sisyphus some centuries later[13].
Art of all kinds - literature through to performance art - is key to survival when we find ourselves up against the wall, especially mentally. It can tell us how our ancestors not just lived but also felt and can often reveal the secret dialogue we all have with ourselves at different stages in life. It can help us feel less alone in the dark (I'm thinking of Akutagawa's suicide note in The Life of a Stupid Man)[14], and for me I seek great comfort in this. Reading especially about the lives of others, lets us know - to cite Meera Syal - that 'Life isn't all ha ha he he'[15] (despite Disney would have us believing differently).

Stumbling on a Cezanne anthology or Van Gogh print in a charity shop is like a gift from above, letting us know what we need to at just the right time, and helping us all make sense of the human struggle and inevitable decline some would choose to ignore. But, of course, there's colour and life that will always endure each and every fate, like in the case of the Italian painter Caravaggio, who had his Renaissance centuries after he'd retired to the heavens.

There's dance, too. We can always see in a performance of many, how we interact together and behave like water, grasses, air, chemistry, etc - perhaps the most spiritual of all the arts' keynotes. We are one and energy cannot be destroyed only recreated.

Erica Crompton

Relationships – for better or for worse

"People are often unreasonable, irrational, and self-centred. Forgive them anyway.
If you are kind, people may accuse you of selfish, ulterior motives. Be kind anyway.
If you are successful, you will win some unfaithful friends and some genuine enemies. Succeed anyway.
If you are honest and sincere people may deceive you. Be honest and sincere anyway.
What you spend years creating, others could destroy overnight. Create anyway.
If you find serenity and happiness, some may be jealous. Be happy anyway.
The good you do today, will often be forgotten. Do good anyway.
Give the best you have, and it will never be enough. Give your best anyway.
In the final analysis, it is between you and God. It was never between you and them anyway.
~Mother Teresa"

Decorating our house with art, and doing an art degree have both punctuated my 30s, after a decade of living with psychosis by this point.

Five years on, aged 33 years, and I had finally been stable on medication and in voluntary work; living in a small flat on a council estate. That's when I met Matt at my volunteering role, remotely. For several years he was my hero. And I think he liked me back. We had a good 6 years together and bought an imposing

Victorian terrace house, which I lovingly decorated with all the best David Shrigley art (a tip from an art dealer and friend in Milan) as well as some of my own custom-made art knock-offs copied directly from the pages of Vogue. But all good things must come to an end, and the artworks provided a bittersweet backdrop – in vermillion and royal blue – for things to unravel.

"We shared a room," he said, calmly and confidently before pausing. "But nothing happened. Jessica's my friend, nothing would ever happen." His eyebrows jutted upwards where they met in the middle. He maintained a furrowed brow as he continued his defence: "I think you're blowing this out of proportion. It was just a really daft mistake... (long pause) What can I do to make you believe me? My commitment to you is right here: in these bricks and mortar. It's you I come home to every night, not my students or anybody else. Your wellbeing. You. You're the most important thing to me."

I listened. There seemed to be a discrepancy between what he was saying and his behaviour. He was still texting Jessica while we holidayed together, and often late at night while I slept. I looked at his face again. A face that was pleading. I couldn't tell if he was lying though.

The stress had been building up between Matt and I in that 6th year, like the final moments of constructing a Jenga tower. For the best part of a year we had argued incessantly, then we'd broken up and now we were going through the painful process of selling our house. It left us with one big dilemma in particular - what to do about the romantic break to Lanzarote we'd booked months earlier.

Sitting in the living room of our old home, weeks before the planned trip, we debated what to do. 'Well we both deserve a holiday after this year' Matt said. 'Maybe we should go together - as friends.' At first I thought he was joking but when I realised he was serious, I agreed it was a good idea. We both desperately needed a break - what better than a few days on the beach with some drinks and seafood - and bizarrely, after breaking up, we'd started to get on much better as we navigated the house sale. Even though we hadn't worked out as a couple, there were plenty of things I still loved about him, so maybe a break-up holiday would help us salvage a friendship.

After we met all those years ago, remotely – when he was based in Derby and I was in here Staffordshire - and as emails bounced between us, we'd hit it off immediately. I loved his commitment to the charity we volunteered at, and his sense of humour and even before we'd met I developed a bit of the big Valium-fuelled crush I mentioned earlier. Later, he moved to Staffordshire for his new job, and we became friends before getting together 3 months later and moving in together 6 months down the line, finally buying our house together in August 2016.

But things went downhill around the time that Matt, who was working as a lecturer, was due to go away for work and asked if I minded him sharing a one-bedroom apartment with his 23-year-old PhD student. 'Err, sure,' I squeaked, not wanting to sound paranoid. But after discussing it with friends, I put my foot down and told him I wasn't comfortable. 'You've got plenty of male friends and I've always been okay with that,' he argued. It escalated into a row and in the end, I went along on the trip too.

This was after I found out that he'd shared apartments with students previously and worse, he'd lied to me about it. For the following months we argued incessantly, often ending in furious outbursts from me. It was very triggering for my psychosis and I found myself seeking support from a Community Psychiatric Nurse who visited me in my home every week for six weeks before concurring that the problem wasn't me – it was Matt. I was changing medication at this time too, under my psychiatrist, due to high prolactin levels. Every day then had started to feeling like I was walking naked through a hail storm in the opposite direction to a strong gale.

Though I still loved him, I'd lost all trust and wasn't sure we could repair that. The subsequent psychosis only made the situation (made it) worse. And the situation made my psychosis worse than that. A few days before our sixth anniversary, tired by the constant battles, Matt suggested we separate. I wanted it to work but agreed it was for the best.

As the holiday to Lanzarote came around and Matt and I got along better, I found myself looking forward to it despite my therapist, friends and family all asking the same question: 'Are you sure you want to go away with your ex?' I have to admit I wasn't 100% sure, but the overriding desire to have a break in the sun got the better of me, and Matt and I were getting along well as friends. Deep down I hoped for a reconciliation but I also knew that this wouldn't happen and nonetheless knew that the trip was a nice way to mark the end of our six-years together.

As we waited for a taxi to the airport, I made a joke and we found ourselves laughing together. 'If we laugh this much the whole week we'll have a great time away,' said Matt. I agreed.

After checking into the hotel, I joked that 'the only double bed we have is perfect for estranged couples' – it was huge. And as the nights passed by I realised my jest was bang on the money as there was never anything going bump between the sheets. But as we got ready for dinner that night, pulling on my best dress, Matt pointed out my label was sticking out and something about the matey way he said it made me think we had already slotted back into being friends. I felt disappointed.

For the rest of the week we sunbathed on the beach, swam in the pool and ate local fish on the coast, chatting happily about our careers and mutual friends. Mostly we avoided discussing our relationship or the breakup but two nights before our holiday ended I couldn't help but make a comment that: "We're not going to rekindle on this holiday are we?" To which Matt replied: "No, we're too far down the line of splitting up now." We sat in silence for 5 minutes after that and we both felt sad things had come to this.

I felt a lot clearer about where I stood with Matt after the holiday, and knowing that I gave the relationship my all makes me happy. I will always care about my ex but it had become clear that without trust a romantic relationship is impossible. But I still see in him the sense of humour and good effort towards others so I feel friends is a good place for us to be. Our break-up will always be tinged with sadness for me, and I discovered how much a 'daft mistake' can hurt someone a great deal. But we've shared good times, made some good mutual friends and if things ever got really bad for either of us I feel we'd both be there for each other.

As we flew home on the last day of the holiday, I felt content. We promised to stay friends while living together in separate rooms and selling our home over the coming months. We finally sold it two months after the holiday. He's moving closer to his new job In Nottingham and I am staying in Staffordshire, having brought myself a small cottage in a village near family.

Since then, I have since started to date other people - I'm yet to find a relationship but I enjoy dating. My psychosis and paranoia improved once I had the left the situation with Matt, too. And although I am sad that our relationship ended, I'm glad we went on that holiday. Though unusual, the time we spent together there made the split amicable and helped us both move on more quickly.

Erica Crompton

The Cottage

There once was a little white cottage.
Home to three;
Two Tom cats and a writer;
the perfect little family.

I can see snow covering the bowling green outside my bedroom window as I write this. After the break-up I invested all the savings I had into a little white cottage in a suburban village outside a local Staffordshire market town. I've been here for around two years and it's tranquil. I have made friends with the neighbours and it's not unusual for us to invite each other over for vegan pizza and cat-fussing. Decorating has been a pleasure and I'm still finding it a lot of fun to lose myself in interior design wish-lists. I've extended my art collection to include a few upcoming artists from London and Bristol's graffiti scenes, too.

But perhaps the best part of life here are my two companions, Caspar and Winter.

I picked them up via Uber on an afternoon after only being in the cottage for 6 weeks. I'd seen them on the Cat's Protection website[16] and instantly fallen in love with them. Finally, after a week of paper shuffling, I was picking them up - the two feline brothers cooped up in a big black cat carrier and scared half to death. We arrived at mine after a 30-minute drive and I put the cat carrier down and unzipped it– food was already laid out for feeding. But they stayed in that cat carrier for about two hours. I decided to give them some space so went and had a bath. Once I returned they'd made their moves: Caspar behind the curtain and Winter hiding in a little space behind the sofa. We sat here for a while, a little circle of eyes on the fireplace. Then I thought I'd give them some more space and went up to my room to make a call to Rockyie, my best friend. About 40 minutes into the call, the cats came in – they'd started to explore! Caspar is the big brother and boldly came in first, followed by his little, white fluffy doppelganger, Winter. When the lights went out, Caspar and Winter made themselves very much at home. 11pm, 12pm, 1am, 2pm….. it seemed every hour, just as I was drifting off to sleep Caspar would pounce on the bed for a kiss and a cuddle. He seemed hyper all night. Winter disappeared and I discovered at 5am next day he'd got himself locked in the airing cupboard. These shy boys were not shy for very long. But they are just so adorable. They seem to like keeping lookout on the window ledges at the front of the house. And they love a little tickle too.

Six weeks into their adoptive home, with me their adoptive mother, and Caspar and Winter were well and truly settled in and had their first outing into the back garden. They say you have to watch the shy ones and that can be said of Winter: he jumped over the 8ft white-washed brick wall and left poor Caspar meowing like a banshee. So I had to go outside and search. Just a couple of minutes into my mission there was a loud bang from the back of the house – the neighbour's garage door, I think. And Winter came flying over the wall and ran inside.

There can be a lot said of owning cats, especially if you have a mental health condition and are on your own. In the 18 months I've been a cat-mum I've not felt lonely once. Instead I've felt loved and there have been moments of pure joy in caring for two feline brothers.

According to research, pets can not only combat said loneliness, but they can also reduce blood pressure and are even said to help you live longer [17].

Over two years later and the cats are great and, while it's been hard to ditch the bacon oatcakes when hungover, I am happy with my decision to go pescatarian, made just two weeks into adopting Caspar and Winter. I just feel since getting to know this pair, that animals have feelings and thoughts and personalities just as we do. So, I don't want to eat them anymore.

Otherwise the cottage is lovely. It's at the foot of a sleepy little road that overlooks the Bowling Green and there's a lilac tree with purple flowers in the forecourt which I hang a bird feeder on. It's been so nice watching the sparrows and blue tits come and go. I even had a robin round last week. I think the cats like to watch the birds too, but they may have less wholesome thoughts about them than me.

Work is slow. Or at least cash is! Covid had struck while writing this book and I'd decided to study a remote master's degree in creative writing. Not only could I study from home and improve my writing game. But it also meant that I could access a Government loan to pay for fees. With what I have left over I've renovated my little kitchen, restoring the quarry tiles to their original state and adding 'shaker' units and a walnut work-surface. I'd decided to splash-out on a Wickes kitchen after hearing an advert on my favourite radio show – Smooth Classics at 7pm on Classic FM.

The take-home of the cottage chapter is that I'm coping on my own, a strong, single independent woman. Even during Covid I've felt myself thriving rather than just surviving. I've learned to enjoy my own company along with my cats to a backdrop of Classic FM which plays through the cottage 9am-8pm.

I'm paying my bills, keeping up with the upkeep of the house, caring for two cats and even getting my five-a-day and regular walks into the countryside. I'm just a couple of miles from Keele Village – a pretty corner of Staffordshire's countryside. And I often take a 9 mile round trip into Keele on my daily exercise allowance. I have always said I like to think I can make it alone. Matt disagreed with this and said I couldn't possibly look after myself. But I'm doing well solo and proving the naysayers wrong – and it feels good.

Erica Crompton

Peer support

"Piglet sidled up to Pooh from behind.
"Pooh!" he whispered.
"Yes, Piglet?"
"Nothing," said Piglet, taking Pooh's paw. "I just wanted to be sure
of you."
— A.A. Milne, The House at Pooh Corner

Friends and family have helped me to care for myself, as well as feel less alone.

Although most of my friends have moved and/or live far away I keep up regular phone calls, visits, gifts and letters.

My dear friend Nutan also lives with a mental health diagnosis. Hers is 'schizo-mania' and she's sometimes in hospital, though her spirit and sully defeated. I met Nutan through a Meetup. com group she created called The London Mental Health Support Group which Nutan ran by herself (18). We became friends here and have been friends for the last decade. We share a diagnosis and more recently a love of cats. The nice thing about support from others with a similar diagnosis is that you can relate to some of the bizarre symptoms we have that others rule-out as 'weird'.

One gripe of every live-together partner or flat-mate I've had has been my ability to get coffee granules everywhere. They say they've never seen anyone make coffee like I do; pouring it straight from the jar and into the cup. Nutan makes coffee like me. The first time she offered me the drink was a punch air moment where all the flack I'd got for pouring coffee from the jar into the cup paled into insignificance. I knew then that we were kindred spirits.

Peer Support in an official sense

Friendships are so important to our wellbeing and to defeat feelings of isolation. Friends can inject humour into hard times, and also provide peer support and comradeship to people like me.

Sometimes a way to start talking is by joining up with others who have similar experiences. You can easily start yourself by signing up to your local 'Recovery College'. 'Recovery Colleges' or 'Wellbeing Academies' began with a bang in Arizona. A mental health inpatient had been forcibly restrained against their will and subsequently complained – the staff were listening. What the patient asked for was to work with, not against, staff and clinicians for optimal outcomes and a less paternal relationship with staff.

From here the concept of Recovery Colleges, now in full-swing in the UK, began to take shape.

For the last several years Recovery Colleges have been popping up all over the UK. There's probably one near you but you don't need to be local or a doctor's referral to attend.

Courses – some just half a day others running for up to 6 months - are set up independently or within NHS Trusts. You do the course which is tailored to your academic level of skills and once you've completed the course you get a certificate at the end.

The independent organisation, charity or Trust will put on courses in a number of places – some in community halls and others set within actual universities.

At the heart of Recovery Colleges is what's called "co-production" where a member of staff works with someone with experience of mental health together to produce better outcomes for mental patients.

Dr Rosie Beck, a Clinical Psychologist for Greater Manchester West Mental Health NHS Foundation Trust (GMW), said: "We promote skills and practices which enable people to take the next step in their recovery, or support others effectively. Our courses are 'co-produced': people with lived experience of mental health difficulty and mental health professionals are 'trainers' in equal partnership, designing and delivering the courses together. This really allows us as trainers and the students to take hold of the value of lived experience and recognise the person's skills separate to their mental health experiences. Service-users, their families, and staff attend the courses together as students, allowing us to learn from each other."

The Central and North West London NHS Foundation Trust Recovery and Wellbeing College is an innovative service that opened in January 2012 as a pilot project offering 10 courses. Over three years on, they've grown and developed and are now delighted to offer over 70 bespoke and pioneering courses to people who use services, practitioners, carers, supporters or people working in the voluntary or private sector, including other CNWL staff.

A service user attending the CNWL Recovery & Wellbeing College echoes the sentiment in course feedback: "Today's experience was very good and informative. Didn't feel condescended to and like a patient. I was a person."

Further North, in Salford, Al, a service user, has been on a two day Living with Anxiety & Depression course and agrees: "I've spent two days with nine other trainees - some staff and, others of us, service users – and all of us keen to learn from each other. What they said had us laughing, welling up and what hair I've got left on my head standing up on. Close friends of mine who've always been there when I slide into depression have said that they can tell "it's so different this time" so I'm chuffed to say the least!"

Recovery Courses are currently being set up at the South Staffordshire & Shropshire NHS Trust too as well as incorporating lived experience into the entire workforce. Acting Recovery College Coordinator, Beth Moody says: "As a person with lived experience of mental health issues and a former user of services here, I have no doubt that our Recovery College will transform lives, and am delighted to now have the opportunity to be involved in a project that will benefit so many people and local communities."

Sue Williams, a peer support worker on an in-patient unit and peer trainer at the Recovery and Wellbeing College in London, explains more about the transition process and from being a 'service user' to a colleague and a member of the workforce which once treated her.

"I have spent the last two and a half years working as a peer support worker on an in-patient unit where I was once detained and working as a peer trainer for the CNWL Recovery and Wellbeing College. I moved from only having contact with professionals as a patient in their services to working alongside mental health practitioners, include working with staff that once treated me.

"Initially I thought this might be a difficult position for both me and those who have worked with me and was worried about how they might respond.

"What I saw was how perceptions and stereotypes relating to mental health could be transformed by having someone that used services now working in services. Many people, staff and services users, said in different ways that they were personally inspired having seen it was possible."

We have a lot to be grateful for, to the patient in Arizona – thanks to them the Recovery Revolution has begun and the colleges are springing up in the UK like Cactus spines.

I have my own local Recovery College in Staffordshire, UK and have made two good friends after 2 days workshops. The NHS Trust here told me they were looking to develop a Recovery College without walls. A spokesman for the college told me this means an alternative to therapeutic intervention and moving towards a focus on education: "The Recovery Approach aims to support and empower individuals to become experts in their own recovery journey, and find meaning in their lived experiences. In this way, the college will embrace a philosophy and culture of hope, control and opportunity. We aim to run a number of courses which will be delivered out in the community, within colleges, libraries and other community venues.

"Due to the core focus around recovery, all courses will be produced and delivered by someone who has professional expertise of the given area and someone who has lived experience of mental health issues (or a mix of both!) The college will also play an important role in the learning and development of staff with regards to how recovery principles are embedded into clinical practice and how staff may best support individuals on their recovery journey. It is important to remember that staff experience their own recovery journey and the culture of hope, control and opportunity can be of benefit to all."

Former Recovery College Co-ordinator at the time I studied there in Staffordshire (and now good friend!) Beth Moody: "As a person with lived experience of mental health issues and a former user of services here, I have no doubt that the Recovery College will transform lives, and am delighted to now have the opportunity to be involved in a project that will benefit so many people and local communities."

In this chapter I pay props to Nutan Modha, the 'High Priestess of Peer Support'. Here I've given her space to write her own story as with psychosis everyone is different and it can never hurt to have added voices of our illness in the mix. Nutan likes writing fairytales with a witty twist and here she's written about Mr Fey, everyone's favourite 'Claus' – Santa – and The World Health Organisation. Nutan is a Londoner currently exiled in Glasgow and like me is a cat Mum to Calico kitty Chica. In her spare time she enjoys writing, and business planning as well sourcing the ultimate red lippy for herself and her friends.

Her story is as follows:

Mr Fey, Santa & The World Health Organisation
By Nutan Modha

Mr Fey had been trying to get his little fob watch to work, as on the night he was talking to Santa, the watch had fallen out of his waistcoat and into a rather large puddle, and were it not for Rudolph The Red Nosed Reindeer - and his bright red nose he would never have found it. Even with something as 'strange' as a flashing red nose, it didn't let him stop, trying to help people. He leads Santa's Sleigh you see. His nose, a beacon of light that guides the other deer. Galloping through snow, hail and also thunder & lightening, where it can get a little tricky. Our wonderful reindeer Rudolf, was able to light the Sleigh, as Mr Fey edged his rather tired arm to prise the small watch, from between the undercarriage and seat. 'Phew' Said Mr Fey 'Now I can get things into perspective' When Mr Fey said things, sometimes 'unusual' things happened. As just when he said that, his tall Top Hat, swiveled round and hooted. Just another day, for Mr Fey. Now at Christmas with Santa, things got terribly muddled with parcel deliveries to all the children in the world. Some parcels were mixed up, but frankly everything from the North Pole was always delightful, so the children were always extremely grateful that he bothered to get the special toys to them, even when it rained. (Bless Big Santa). Remember there are toys for children. And there are toys for adults. They are two different things entirely. Rudolph was able to steer through the most treacherous of weather. Rain, hail or shine. That was Rudolph. He never let Santa down. Like your very best friend in life, they would always be there. Sometimes you may not see them, very much like busy Pixies, Elves and 'The Little People'. But they were always there. Just like all the trees in the world. They stayed firm and ready to branch, flower and blossom. Always ready for a painter to paint. With all these selfies, these days, Tree Painting was forgotten. Mr Fey sighed, a sad sigh: "What to do Santa?" Santa and Mr Fey & The Minions had been going through a list of children with the help of the World Health Organisation, Bill Gates & Tom Jones as they had all kindly helped Santa use spreadsheets from Microsoft Office. He had all the names and addresses in one super-extensive file. He was tickled pink, as his life was a lot easier now - and all he had to do was to use Alexa and ask if the road, desert or igloo had been good in 2020. Alexa was also able to help (but occasionally couldn't understand North Pole Language). Mr Fey had just finished his counselling session with a poor Ogre from the Middle East who had a disagreement with a Troll from China, and they couldn't see eye to eye. Ogres only had one eye, so the reconciliation was very important to him. The Troll had become upset, when the Ogre became clumsy with his gardening and had been planting kelp for the nymphs and lettuce for the rabbits, and had accidentally sat on a bridge, thereby breaking it. The troll had lost his occupation and couldn't find another bridge before Christmas. As you can imagine, it was a rather long arbitration. However, there was a solution - a Troll in Brussels had offered his bridge to help the family in St Petersburg, Russia and a nice Christmas was had by all. This is how Mr Fey worked. Everybody needed to win, and when you work in an Office of The Unseen, Invisible & Magical representing England, Scotland & Wales

& Elsewhere : you had to make that 'situation' always be on the top of any list, that was made by Mr Fey. This meant 'win, win' - Everybody wins. Very much like a Tombola at Jumble Sales. The Cornettos, were the last on the list for Santa, as he could shoot straight back to the North Pole after the very tip of Scotland. And he had been asking questions about Young Isabella and Young Joshua. "It says here, they've been running round the house" Said Santa. My Fey nodded earnestly "Yes, It's because of COVID Santa, the children have been playing outside, but they can't run in straight lines ….." Mr Fey was looking at his watch and was trying to get Santa to understand why Joshua had progressed from drumming to running. "Does Mrs Cornetto and Arthur still manage to do adult things during COVID, like paperwork ?" asked Santa "Oh Yes Santa" said Mr Fey "It only takes two minutes to ask Joshua to stop running round in circles" he protested. "But then he runs the other way " said Santa looking at the spreadsheet. "The Cornettos have a garden Santa, but Joshua is still so Young Santa and you know what little boys are made off ….." "Santa began reading an old poem English poet Robert Southey (1774–1843)" He cleared his throat so he could hear himself : "What are little boys made of? What are little boys made of? Snips and snails and puppy-dogs' tails That's what little boys are made of. What are little girls made of? What are little girls made of? Sugar and spice And everything nice [or "all things nice"] That's what little girls are made of" Mr Fey looked at his watch, it was past twelve already and he was going to miss his Ship. Santa was busy with the Khans next door, and couldn't answer. As he tried to bundle as many presents as he could, he stopped to answer Mr Fey. Mr Fey was now running very late. He had a lecture in Kazakhstan which was about the finest kind of Leprechauns. "Santa, Have you made a decision yet ? The Cornetto's have tried so hard and because of COVID…." Santa interrupted and said "Oh My Fey, you know my rules and you know every child always gets a present. I've sent our special Royal Mail Postman to try and get the late presents out, so let's wait and see if the grown ups can be good or naughty this year." Mr

Fey smiled a hu-mungous smile, and knew Santa had cracked it. Away went Mr Fey wishing Rudolph and The Santa Gang a very Merry Christmas and in two shakes of a rat's tail, he was on his way to Kazakhstan.

My little magazine

"Look at little closer around the gutter.
When you finally hit the bottom.
Kinship and friends await you here;
Together we'll gaze at the stars."

Helping friends find their voices is something that's very important to me. So is reaching out to give a helping hand to people who may feel blue. In the summer of 2018 I lost not one, not two, not three, but four childhood friends who took their lives at their own hands. While none of us were close at the time they were on my social media pages where I campaign to raise awareness of mental illnesses. With this in mind I couldn't help but wonder if I could have been doing more to help others. I wondered to distraction and in the following weeks finally decided to take action. I sent an email to all my contacts expressing my desire to share my own experience of attempting suicide and details on how I came to see the light with others, in order to help them. I also expressed that it was by using my skills as a writer and former editor that I so wished to help – I decided to make a zine, and would anyone like to be involved?

Emails come and go and I didn't expect many people to respond, but they did and enthusiastically, too. Within days I was soon booked for the upcoming December to give a talk on suicide prevention to 300 mental health professionals, locally. And a really cool graffiti artist from London had kindly offered to donate some artwork to my zine. Other friends in the email hoped to write for the magazine to pass the lessons they learnt from overcoming adversity or suicidal thoughts to others. My 'Hopezine' was conceived… and I planned to launch it at the local suicide prevention conference I was booked to speak at in December.

The talk went well though I was racked with nerves and my voice trembled as a relayed the details of my suicide attempt to a football stand packed with 300 people. I also had a small table in a room full of small suicide prevention charities to share Hopezine on which was less jitter-inducing. I spent £200 designing and printing just 75 copies of my little zine with the cool graffiti artwork on the cover and posted spare copies to friends and family, as well as the local police station and psychiatric hospital.

The zine looked cute and it filled me with a lot of pride: it was a pink 'Mr Messy' on the cover with the title in bold black letters, HOPEZINE, the 'O' filled in a fun, bright and zesty yellow. Over just 12 glossy and colourful pages, friends had written their stories of hope, of overcoming suicide attempts and suicidal thoughts to pass on rays of light to others. 'Rays of Light Amid The Darkness' was actually the tagline on the cover.

Someone from the local council expressed and interest in the zine and the interest turned into hard cash the following year. Sadly funds from the council only lasted for one issue but meant I was able to pay each contributor £20 for their words and photographs which felt amazing.

It was after the second issue came out that I started working with Matt, another friend from school – a former flame from the days where sex was a distant dream. Matt also knew the friends from school and, like them, I'd stayed in touch on social media. Matt had seen my mental health writing and campaigning and invited me to work for him on his latest wellbeing project for businesses. I did and it was fun, rewarding work. It was also pretty amusing seeing my old school friend in the guise of a successful business man, all suited and booted in grey hues. In his heyday he was a sulky grungy Pearl Jam fan and even dreadlocked his blonde curls. Today he slicks his curls to the side and manages his 1000-man-strong business alongside family life.

It was after successfully completing this wellbeing project for Matt's company that he so kindly offered to sponsor Hopezine with 4 consecutive adverts on the back page of the zine. So, Hopezine could continue its quarterly print run for another year.

It seemed a good job was made of those subsequent Hopezines. Fast forward to the present, and at the time of writing Matt's business, Fintel, is up for sponsoring Hopezine long-term as part of its ongoing impact work in the community.

It's not just helping others, it helps me keep busy and enables me to connect with a wider community in a meaningful way. I really love the story of how 2 former school friends came together later in life to help others feel happier. It's sweet, and joyful.

Over the coming years I plan to develop Hopezine into a really fun and glossy mental wellbeing magazine. More pages, more artwork, more impact and thanks to Matt more cash, too.

We've talked about taking it into schools and it would be really nice to combine it with my public speaking and experience teaching writing to help school children write their first ever published articles.

Children are the future after all.

Apart from my magazine, I write for newspapers and magazines. It's a wonderful way to making a living. I love crafting articles and telling stories. And when I write about my mental health journalistically it gives me a passport to interview top psychiatrists and mental health professionals – helping me learn about psychosis and myself, with each new piece.

It's become quite ritualistic: I fling open my floral bedroom curtains at 5am, it is usually still dark. Then I open the window and let the early morning birdsong flood my space. I'll drink a couple of rocket-fuel-strength coffees, and pull up my laptop into bed where I begin work. There's something quite meditative about writing and when I'm anxious I will also try to write then to soothe me. A little later in this book I'll talk about what I've learned from writing a memoir, personally and spiritually.

The other thing I love about writing is how lo-fi it is. All I need is Word and an internet connection for research. I also write in a journal. I've journals going back to 2011 with my little daily 'to-do' lists to remind me what I've been up to and what I've been working on. Shopping lists, a dream that's lingered from the night before, poems of heartache, goals and wish lists – they're all written down in my shabby but swirly handwriting.

I've made some really good friends and found meaningful connections through my work, whether just online or in real life. I met Matt, my long-term partner, through editing a newsletter.

I remember when I first started out I got fired from an American magazine I was freelancing for and the experience really shook me up. So I confided in a fellow writer, Carlo, who I worked with on the fashion desk at The Daily Telegraph. His email reply came reassuringly fast and was equally as soothing. Writing to me from his art-filled apartment in Milan, as I bemoaned being laid on the ground, he said: "Look very closely at the gutter in which you lay because here you'll find me."

Finding myself spiritually

"The spring offers hope.
In new beginnings.
We have to begin at an ending;
and make that fresh start."

Let's get spiritual

I recently had a meeting with a shaman and felt that she could have helped me, with her shamanistic techniques, to visualise all the harmful guilt I'd racked up, to locate and identify it abstractly as a 'Power Animal' – and therefore deal with it. It doesn't surprise me that more and more people experiencing psychotic episodes like mine and turning to spiritual practises to help them deal with their demons. I hear in Brazil they even use psychics alongside psychiatrists to treat severe mental illnesses like mine.

It is also nice to think that the sunshine is always here, for all of us – no matter who or where we are and no matter what and why we've done it.

During my time in the rundown flat-share where I attempted suicide I'd had a dream where I was flying that felt very powerful even on waking. My dream was of flying and hammering clouds from the sky. With hindsight I now see this as a powerful, spiritual premonition and one that sticks by me as a close and reassuring friend. In my dream I was in full control of my life and knocking out clouds from the sky to reveal sunshine. Isn't it lovely then that I attribute the sunshine with saving my life immediately after? In the grip of paranoid schizophrenia, I had little control but I believe the dream and my destiny is bigger than the practical.

I was alone in the dream, as I was in waking life, wandering the streets. Then I looked up at the sunshine and decided to fly up to it. I have never flown in dreams before, but I could in this one. I had a sparkly hammer and started to knock clouds out of the sky so the sun could shine in all its golden glory.

After the dream I did make an attempt to suicide but it was the spring sunshine appearing through the window that stopped me, made me think twice, and reach out to the emergency services. I have always liked to think that the dream was a message from above. I realise such a blind faith in an entity that has no science base could be the cause of derision and mocking (and yes my faith has been mocked and even compared to spaghetti monsters at times).

Regardless of the naysayers I have since continued spiritual practice – including meditation and shamanic sound baths - as a way to cope with my condition, and the snakes and ladders of life. I consider myself 'spiritually agnostic' because I respect and am interested in all kinds of ways of seeing and believing. There's a growing movement of mental health service users who campaign for a holistic approach to their treatments, and also see their breakdowns as a 'spiritual emergency'.

But I do feel it was a faith that enabled me to make the crucial call that day and for that reason I continue to believe in the higher forces, in fate, keep a dream journal and sometimes see a Jungian analysis to decipher what my dreams mean. They're often an important message from my subconscious which can help me in my waking life.

Far from making my psychosis worse, I believe that being spiritual has helped me deal with my mental illness and soothe me during times of distress. Living with psychosis has taught me that sometimes the worst things can also be the best as it's helped me relate to others, make friends and carve a career as a writer for myself. I focus on challenging stereotypes and stigma which reminds me of that dream where I was knocking clouds down.

Ultimately, I found my own faith during my journey with managing schizophrenia.

Sometimes our silver linings outweigh the misfortunes that accompany them.

After the dream, after reading books on shamanism and Buddhism, I get it. I broke down good and hard but 10 years later I now believe there was a meaning to this and I also believe I have pieced myself back together as a much better person. Sometimes we can build castles with the stones life throws at us.

Summary

The following summary is a reflection based on 2 chapters from what I hope has been an inspiring memoir of living with psychosis and what I've learned from writing it as well as managing it for over two decades. It goes a little further than just the 'self' as a diagnosis though. For example, I hope the happy and fruitful experiences I outline on the Hare Krishna farm are an example of not just how spirituality can soothe someone on the first steps to recovery but also how some long periods of time I've had on this recovery journey can be experienced without symptoms of psychosis. Like my life, the good, the bad and the ugly are all covered here in equal measure. My memoir is aimed at young people and I've written it like a magazine: crammed with first-person features, expert tips, and the prose is short and to the point (or 'Literary Journalism' as my mentor tells me).

My found theories of the self

In *Writing: Self and Reflexivity*,[19] Hunt et al. write that the English Romantic poets of the early 19th century, such as Blake and Wordsworth, were largely opposed to what they saw as the mechanistic nature of Enlightenment thought and its dehumanising social consequences in the Industrial Revolution of the late 18th century. Instead they believed that humans had a central essence. They believed in a pure spirit whose imaginative powers put us in touch with an ultimate reality beyond the everyday world. Looking within, I'm inclined to agree with this statement. In the previous chapters of my book 'pure spirit' is something

I search for and ultimately find in myself in the conclusion: "I broke down good and hard but 10 years later I now believe there was a meaning to this and I also believe I have pieced myself back together as a much better person." Digging a little deeper, my pastimes have included Buddhism practise, too. So in addition to actively seeking this 'pure spirit' I'd add in some Buddhist 'non-self' to how I've come to construct my 'self'. Writing in Frontier Psychology Yung-Jong[20] introduces us to this concept of 'non-self' that can help eliminate desires and ego in the pursuit of global happiness and universal peace. Yung writes: "The maintenance and strength of self is a very core concept in Western psychology and is particularly relevant to egoism, a process that draws on the hedonic principle in pursuit of desires. Contrary to this and based on Buddhism, a non self-cultivating process aims to minimize or extinguish the self and avoid desires, leading to egolessness or selflessness." I've found myself writing this memoir from a place within that exists in my mind somewhere between the Romantic poets and the Buddhists. It's nice to be beautiful but even more beautiful to be nice. I've also found with a mix of sickness benefits, student loans and self-employed work as a writer I'm able to live a comfortable life. A life that is good enough. I'm not sure I'd have the means to survive if I was completely without ego and totally self-sacrificing. Payments for writing assignments, book deals and benefits often have to be fought for with an ego. As for the 'pure spirit' and the essence of imagination I have found both these in my writing in the form of Mihaly Csikszentmihalyi's concept of 'flow'[21] a mental state in which a person performing an activity is fully immersed in a feeling of energised focus, full involvement, and enjoyment in the process of the activity. Flow is characterized by complete absorption in what one does. Writing (as does reading) settles me. I've found my flow and ability to write at its best at 5am when I awake all angst-ridden. All that angsty energy is best channelled into my writing at this time – the ideas come to fizzle and pop to the fore after my early morning coffee and a restful night's slumber.

How I decided to explore 'spiritual self' by telling this story.

In this reflection I've been inspired by spiritual memoirs, including 'Spirit of Garbo'[22] about the spiritual life and magical ways of the movie star. In this memoir we discover lots of Garbo's beliefs through her poetry, letters and conversations. "She assimilated Theosophical ideas into her own world view," the author notes. I've written up my experiences of staying with a group of monks on a Hare Krishna-run farm in a matter-of-fact way. In addition, I'd also learnt from reading Katie Mottram's spiritual memoir[23] that sometimes being spiritual is as much about how we choose to frame our experiences, rather than having our own stories of seeing or feeling ghosts or hearing voices. In this regard I've chosen to write about my experiences and purposefully frame them as spiritual, or at least spiritual/meaningful, to me. I elaborated on how the 'dark of the night' seemed so magical, so mystical here: "There was something about the late night – of sitting under a canopy of stars as the sunset and the moon rose, which seemed so spiritual to me.

The animal was central to the evening – it was as if he was part of our group. It felt magical and very meaningful to be sat with like-minded friends and a sheep that evening as we gradually became covered in the dark of the night."

How it felt to write about this time?

For the introduction to each new chapter I've tried to take a playful approach that's inspired by the poetry of Muldoon[24]. I spent some time jotting down words that have strong connotations for me and my family who I hope will one day read my memoirs. First I experimented with word play around a family joke that we share about the local farmer's wife:

The farmer's wife
Adult to child:
Come massage my feet!
They're full of hard skin
Hard skin, cracked
Corny plates of meat
What are her feet like, asks Dad?

I then applied this approach to the four-line stanzas to introduce the themes in general for each chapter to lead the reader in with an idea of what's to follow.

According to Winnicott's theory of playing[25], "Psychotherapy takes place in the two areas of overlap; the patient and the therapist. Psychotherapy has to do with two people playing." I've used this 'two-man play' theory when sourcing quotes from the monks on the farm for my memoir. They're always very appreciative of my writing about them, which I've been doing for a decade now. Being 'the inquisitive reporter' as a form of play works for me here. It also helps that I have a notebook or professional façade as a boundary between myself and interviewee – people are more reserved about overstepping personal space if that's a professional boundary in place. To gather my quotes and bring them up to date, I simply dropped the head of the eco farm an email and asked if I could briefly interview him over the phone about motoring and how he drives mindfully which I felt may surprise readers to know that the modern monk drives a Landrover. It's also worth noting that during my time writing for The Mail on Sunday I was told to always get quotes from audio. The Mail on Sunday health editor, Barney Calman, told me: "People rarely sound as they are in real life over email. Always phone or meet people in person for quotes if you can – it will make the text more authentic."

How I shaped and structured the story

I read a few memoirs to help inspire my structure. Spirit of Garbo by Moon Laramie and Mending the Gap by Katie Mottram. My memoirs are only novella-length. I've intentionally written them with the short attention spans associated with psychosis in mind. It is a medical memoir with practical advice and tips for people with psychosis, after all. Each chapter is just under a 10 minute read at 1500 words, the average length of a newspaper 'long read'. At the time of finalising my first draft I'd received some feedback from a literary agent, The Good Literary Agency, who said: "While we enjoyed your fresh approach to an important subject, we would encourage you to look again at the structure of the overall work as it read to us more like vignettes than it did a singular text exploring the subject in detail. In truth, we struggled to visualise the format and style you propose for The Mind Surfer and wonder if some further clarity here, perhaps throughout your proposal, could help." I've tried to address this in rewriting each chapter for this assignment. I feel without wanting to rewrite the memoirs from scratch it maybe a smarter approach to 'rebrand' it as a collection of stories 'from a journalist with a history of schizophrenia.' This in mind, I've rewritten each chapter for this submission as stand-alone packages that can be read as short essays or vignettes. The book is designed to be an easy read for people of all reading abilities and I hope this comes across in my work.

How I found an appropriate narrative voice?

I've always written words as close to my thoughts, and in a succinct and easy to read way. I've drawn a lot on old memories and updated them as memories sharpen with some reflection. It's interesting to note in Paul John Eakin's Storied selves[26]: "From Wordsworth right up to Lively, epiphanies of recall like Proust's abound in autobiography: "I see still the bright flower-laden trees," such ecstasies notwithstanding, students of memory today hold that past experience is necessary, both psychologically and neurologically – constructed anew in each memory event or act of recall." I've had to roll up my sleeves to retain memory and especially writing about direct experience of psychosis. Psychosis has a negative impact on memory[27]. However I've kept old journal notes, called up my subjects to inject fresh quotes and there's also been past articles I've written that have parts from the 'cutting room floor' that can still be used as my co-author Professor Stephen Lawrie did with our debut book The Beginner's Guide to Sanity[28]. That's a drawback to memory. However improvising landscapes, my own thoughts and feelings has also been possible. Improvisation has also played a nice counter-narrative when I write at a time my mental health is strong. What I've also enjoyed about the memoir is the editing and rewriting parts. It's also been possible to 'write myself sane' for the purpose of challenging stigma to violent stereotypes of people with psychosis in public discourse. In this regard focusing on the more every day, less lurid aspects of my life has been rewarding.

From playfulness with interactions with Hare Krishna monks, to writing a book that the monk's will say is 'good for my karma', Mind Surfing is essentially an exploration of my 'self' as a 'pure spirit' seeker with a makeshift grounding in Buddhist principles and philosophy. This book is also an exercise in helping others in crisis with psychosis or looking for guidance or ideas on what steps they can take to recover themselves and get 'steady'. While my memory is impacted by psychosis after a decade of campaigning, writing and delivering talks on managing psychosis I'm able to identify and recall what has and has not resonated with myself and others. Writing as a vehicle to help others has been, and I hope will continue to be, a sound way to play my 'self' forward.

About the Author

Erica Crompton holds a master's degree in creative writing from Teesside University and undergraduate degrees in journalism and another in fine art. She's written about mental health for The New York Times, The Mail on Sunday, The Guardian, The Independent, Metro Online, The Lancet Psychiatry & Happiful Magazine. She's also an avid fashion writer and has worked full-time in this capacity for John Lewis, as well as freelance for The Daily Telegraph, Vice, Nylon and Vogue.co.uk. In addition she gives keynote speeches across the UK on living with psychosis and schizophrenia which includes talks for schools. She has a history of paranoid schizophrenia, but today is schizo-affective, stable and working part-time.

Erica Crompton

Acknowledgements

Erica would like to thank Consuelo at Victorina Press for the opportunity to publish her memoirs and Jacqueline Hartshill and Dr Sophie Nicholls for their esteemed feedback and edits. Special thanks to peer support Guru Nutan Modha for her friendship and the guest chapter, chapter 9.

Erica Crompton

Bibliography

1. Beards, S., Gayer-Anderson, C., Borges, S., Dewey, M. E., Fisher, H. L., & Morgan, C. (2013). Life events and psychosis: A review and meta-analysis. Schizophrenia Bulletin, 39(4), 740–747. https://doi.or/0.109/chbu

2. Cutting, J (1979). Memory in functional psychosis. Journal of Neurology, Neurosurgery, and Psychiatry, 1979, 42, 103 1- 10 37 1031.full.pdf (bmj.com)

3. Anon. (2021) Delusional Disorder. Clevelandclinic. org Delusional Disorder: Treatments, Causes, Types & Diagnosis (clevelandclinic.org)

4. Anon (2021) Psychosis (Fact sheet). Mind What is psychosis? | Mind

5. Lawrie, S; Crompton, E. (2020) The Beginner's Guide to Sanity

6. Hjorthøj C, Stürup AE, McGrath JJ et al (2017). Years of potential life lost and life expectancy in schizophrenia: a systematic review and meta-analysis. Lancet Psychiatry. 2017 Apr;4(4):295-301

7. World Wide Organisation of Organic Farming Opportunities, UK. WWOOF UK, Chapter 1, Chapter 2

7a. World Wide Organisation of Organic Farming Opportunities, UK. WWOOF UK, Chapter 3, Chapter 4, Chapter 5

8. Anon. (2021) Mental Health statistics: children and young people. The Mental Health Foundation Mental health statistics: children and young people | Mental Health Foundation

9. Yotka, S. (2017). How Sara Ziff and More Than 40 Other Models Are Leading the Charge Against Eating Disorders. Vogue.com. A New Study Takes on Eating Disorders in Modeling | Vogue

10. Schizophreic.nyc

11. Fandabby.net

12. Phillips MR, Yang G, Li S, Yue L. (2004) Suicide and the unique prevalence pattern of schizophrenia in mainland China: A retrospective observational study. Lancet 364: 1062–1068 [PubMed]

13. Camus, A. (2018). The Myth of Sisyphus. Penguin Vintage.

14. Akutagawa. (2015). The Life of a Stupid Man. Penguin Little Black Classics

15. Syal, M . (2000). 'Life isn't all ha ha he he'. Black Swan books.

16. Cats Protection | UK's Largest Feline Welfare Charity

17. Buckland, D. (2019). Mental health: Why pets are vital in fight against loneliness. The Daily Express. Mental health: Why pets are vital in fight against loneliness | Express.co.uk

18. www.meetup.com

19. Hunt, C. and Sampson, F. (2006). Writing : self and reflexivity. Houndmills, Basingstoke, Hampshire ; New York: Palgrave.

20. Yung-Jong Shiah, (February 2016). From Self to Nonself: The Nonself Theory, Front Psychol. Published online 2016 Feb doi: 10.3389/fpsyg.2016.00124 [accessed 2nd February 2021]

21. Nakamura, J. and Csikszentmihalyi, M. (n.d.). The Concept of Flow Optimal Experience and Its Role in Development. [online]. Available at: https://nuovoeutile.it/wp-content/uploads/2015/12/2002-Flow.pdf [Accessed 2 Feb. 2021].

22. Laramie, M. (2018). Spirit of Garbo. London: Martin Firrell Company Ltd.

23. Mottram, K. (2014). Mend the Gap. Rethink Press.

24. BBC. (2021). Paul Muldoon. [online] Available at: https://www.bbc.co.uk/programmes/m000rv75 [Accessed 2 Feb. 2021].

25. Winnicott, D.W. (2005). Playing and reality. London ; New York: Routledge.

26. Paul John Eakin and Cornell University Press (2005). How our lives become stories : making selves. Ithaca, Ny ; London: Cornell University Press, [Post.

27. ScienceDaily. (n.d.). Brain marker of poor memory in schizophrenia patients identified: Possible key to understanding, treating cognitive symptoms of disease. [online] Available at: https://www.sciencedaily.com/releases/2016/04/160404143843.htm.

28. Crompton, E. (2020). BEGINNER'S GUIDE TO SANITY : a self-help book for people with psychosis.(June 2020) Hammersmith Health Books.